MW00667638

Ocean Life
Activity Book

Author	Linda Milliken
Editor	Kathy Rogers
Page Design	Linda Milliken
Cover Design	Imaginings

METRIC CONVERSION CHART

Refer to this chart when metric conversions are not found within the activity.

¼ tsp	=	1 ml	350° F =		180° C
½ tsp	=	2 ml	375° F =		190° C
1 tsp	=	5 ml	400° F =		200° C
1 Tbsp	=	15 ml	425° F =		216° C
¼ cup	=	60 ml	1 inch	=	2.54 cm
⅓ cup	=	80 ml	1 foot	=	30 cm
½ cup	=	125 ml	1 yard	=	91 cm
1 cup	=	250 ml	1 mile	=	1.6 km
1 oz.	=	28 g			
1 lb.	=	.45 kg			

EP116 • ©1998 Edupress, Inc™ • P.O. Box 883 • Dana Point, CA 92629
www.edupressinc.com
ISBN 1-56472-116-7
Printed in USA

 # Table of Contents

• *Starfish*
by Edith Hacher Hurd;
Harper LB 1962. (2-4)
The structure of the starfish, its eating habits, and its reproductive pattern are simply explained.

• *Discovering Jellyfish*
by Marianda Macquitty;
Watts LB 1989. (3-5)
The physical characteristics of jellyfish are covered, with material on how they live.

• *Hermit Crabs*
by Sylvia A. Johnson;
Lerner LB 1989. (3-5)
An introduction to hermit crabs with striking photos.

• *Dolphin Adventure: A True Story*
by Wayne Grover;
Greenwillow 1990. (3-5)
An encounter with wild dolphins off the Florida coast.

• *Where the Waves Break: Life at the Edge of the Sea*
by Anita Malnig;
Carolrhoda LB 1985. (3-5)
An introduction to life at the sea's edge, including descriptions of starfish, brittle stars, snails, and seaweed.

• *A Sea Full of Sharks*
by Betsy Maestro;
Scholastic 1990. (3-6)
An informative look at this feared but fascinating creature.

• *Crystal: The Story of a Real Baby Whale*
by Karen C. Smyth;
Down East paper 1986. (3-6)
The first year in the life of a humpback whale.

• *A Coral Reef*
by Norman Barrett;
Watts LB 1991. (3-5)
This introduction to the composition and construction of coral reefs contains many colored pictures.

• *Great Whales: The Gentle Giants*
by Patricia Lauber;
Henry Holt LB 1991. (3-5)
Characteristics and habits of great whales are explored as well as a look at whale hunting and conservation efforts.

• *Monsters of the Deep*
by Norman Barrett;
Watts LB 1991. (3-5)
The great sea predators and large sea mammals are introduced through many pictures and extensive captions.

• *Beneath the Waves: Exploring the Hidden World of the Kelp Forest*
by Norbert Wu;
Chronicle 1992. (3-7)
The undersea kelp forests are the food source for many sea creatures such as jellyfish, snails, sea otters, and others.

• *Tentacles: The Amazing World of Octopus*
by James Martin;
Crown LB 1993. (4-6)
In addition to the octopus, this account covers the nautilus, squid, cuttlefish, and other cephalopods.

• *Don't Blink Now! Capturing the Hidden World of Sea Creatures*
by Ann Downer;
Watts LB 1991. (4-8)
Chapters on survival and reproduction enhance this chatty, well-photographed look at marine animals.

 # Glossary

baleen—horny, elastic material hanging in fringed sheets from the upper jaw or palate of some whales.

baleen whales—the group of whales that have baleen instead of teeth; this group includes right whales, grey whales, rorquals, blue whales, Bryde's whales, fin whales, humpback whales, Minke whales, and Sei whales.

benthos—plants and animals that live on the ocean bottom, sometimes attached in one position throughout their lives.

bivalve—any mollusk having a shell of two parts hinged together.

blubber—a layer of fat beneath a whale's skin that serves as insulation against the cold water.

coral reef—a limestone formation in the sea made of the skeletons of millions of polyps.

ecosystem—all the animals, plants, and bacteria that make up a particular community living in a certain environment.

fins—movable structures on the outside of a fish's body that help it swim and keep its balance.

gill—the breathing organ of most animals that live in water such as fish and crustaceans.

habitat—the place where an animal or plant is normally found.

holdfast—rootlike part of seaweed that anchors it to a solid object and keeps it from being swept away.

lateral line system—special sense organ of a fish that allows it to sense changes of movement in the water through vibration.

luminescence—any giving off of light caused by the absorption of radiant energy.

mantle—skin-like organ of a mollusk that makes the shell by secreting liquid shell materials; the mantle on mollusks with no shells (octopus, squid) forms a tough cover around body organs.

nekton—fish and other animals that have the ability to swim freely in water without the help of currents.

phonations—sounds used by whales to communicate with one another.

photosynthesis—the formation in green plants of organic substances from carbon dioxide and water in the presence of light and chlorophyll.

protective coloration—a form of camouflage in which the animal is colored to blend in with its environment, making it difficult to spot.

protective resemblance—a form of camouflage in which the animal's body is shaped like things in its environment.

radula—the ribbon of teeth in a univalve that works like a rough file and tears apart the animal's food.

regeneration—the ability to regrow lost body parts; starfish and other echinoderms are able to regenerate lost arms and other body parts.

scales—the thin, flat, overlapping, horny plates forming the outer covering of many fishes and reptiles.

sea star—another name for a starfish.

siphon—muscular tube through which bivalves get oxygen and food.

spawn—the eggs of fishes, mollusks, amphibians, and other animals; they are usually produced in great numbers and they have no shells.

toothed whales—the group of whales with teeth; this group includes sperm whales, beaked whales, belugas, narwhals, dolphins, and porpoises.

tube feet—tube-like structures on an echinoderm's body used for moving, feeding, breathing, and sensing; they usually project from the body in rows.

univalve—mollusk having a one-piece shell.

4

Habitats

Information

A special set of relations develops between living inhabitants and their environment. Every marine animal or plant prefers a particular *habitat*. It shares the habitat with other animals and plants in an *ecosystem*. The types of plants and animals that live within these different ocean zones and habitats vary greatly. Most of the life in the sea is found in the upper 300 feet (91.4 m) of water. This is as far as the sun's rays can penetrate with enough strength to support plant life.

Along the shore and in shallow waters live worms, crustaceans, and kelp. The open sea is populated by familiar fish such as sharks and halibut who race about not far from the surface. The greater the depth, the fewer the living creatures. At its greatest depths the ocean is a world of total darkness inhabited by a sparse population of plants and animals, sometimes visible only because of their *luminescence*.

Project

Work in cooperative groups to create murals that reflect a variety of ocean habitats and zones.

Materials

- Habitat Starter Cards, following
- Butcher paper
- Paint, brushes
- Scissors
- Glue
- Crepe, tissue, construction paper
- Glow-in-the-dark paint
- Photographic ocean life resource books

Directions

1. Divide into cooperative groups. Cut apart and review a Habitat Starter Card with each group.

2. Give each group a large sheet of butcher paper on which to create a mural. Group members should read the starter information then research their assigned habitat more completely. They may use a variety of materials to recreate their assigned ocean habitat. As the ocean study continues, the murals may be added to. Encourage the creation of dimension through the use of crumpled tissue paper, sponges, and other recycled art materials students find in the classroom or bring from home.

Habitat Starter Cards

TIDE POOL

▼ **PLANT LIFE:**
  Seaweed, kelp, moss, algae

▼ **ANIMAL LIFE:**
  Sea anemones and sponges; tiny kelp crabs; barnacles and mussels attached to rocks; worms, snails, oysters

SHALLOW SHORES

▼ **PLANT LIFE:**
  Abundant plant life

▼ **ANIMAL LIFE:**
  Soft worms, crabs, lobsters, hermit crabs, starfish, sea urchins, mussels, starfish; shelled animals, sponges

OPEN OCEAN

▼ **PLANT LIFE:**
  Plankton is sparse; very little plant growth

▼ **ANIMAL LIFE:**
  Jellyfish and comb jellies, giant ocean sunfish; sharks, tuna, swordfish, whales, squid, dolphins, and other sporting fish

CORAL REEF

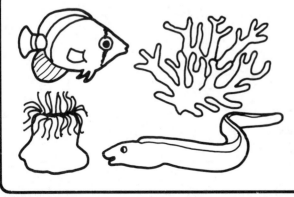

▼ **PLANT LIFE:**
  Plankton is sparse; very little plant growth

▼ **ANIMAL LIFE:**
  Coral formations in many shades; octopuses hunting crabs and eels snaking through holes in the reef; brightly colored fishes, starfish, mollusks, and sea anemones

Reproduce pattern page for activities noted throughout the book.

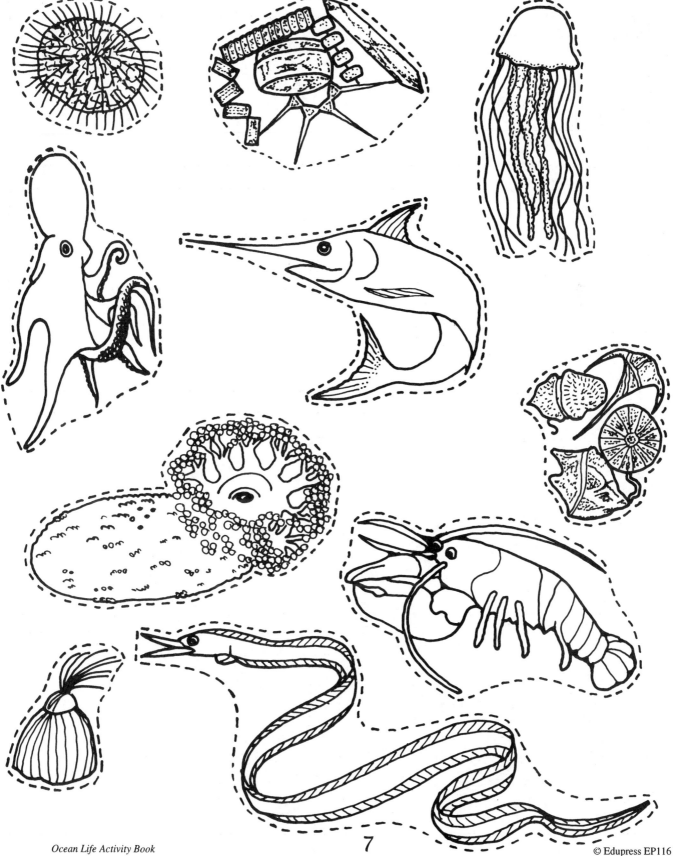

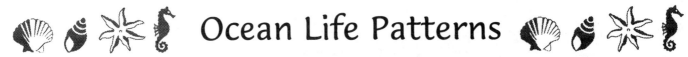 

Ocean Life Patterns

Reproduce pattern page for activities noted throughout the book.

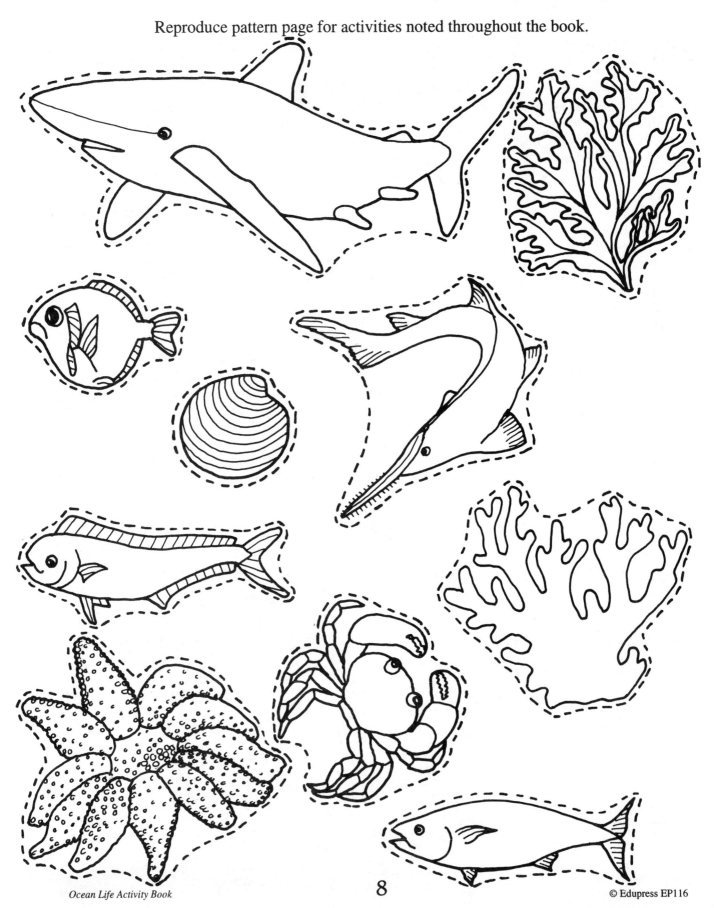

Algae

Information

Any plant that grows in the sea can be called a seaweed but it usually refers to algae. The upper layer of the ocean is populated with trillions of these tiny single-celled plants. Algae use sunlight through *photosynthesis* to produce food and oxygen, which purifies the water. Groups of algae form an abundance of marine plants, called plankton, a major food source for ocean animals. Scientists estimate that phytoplankton produce more than three-quarters of the earth's oxygen!

Algae have no true stems, roots, leaves, or seeds. They grow quickly, carpeting the area in which they live with color. Green algae thrive on sunlit shores. Red algae form crusts in tide pools, but they can also live as far down as 200 feet (61 m). Brown algae are suited for shores and lesser depths. Their tough leathery structures can withstand surf, sun, and tides. Some blue-green algae form slippery dark coatings on rocks along the shore.

Project

Sponge-paint a picture of one type of marine algae. Examine the painting for single-celled algae.

Materials

- Brown, red, green, and blue tempera paint
- Sponges
- Paper plates
- White construction paper
- Magnifying glass

Directions

1. Pour tempera paints by color onto paper plates.

2. Choose a color to paint. A blue-green combination is a choice as well.

3. Dip the sponge into the paint. Cover the entire surface of the construction paper by gently pressing the paint-coated sponge against it.

4. Use a magnifying glass to examine the paint-coated paper. Imagine you are looking at algae and each small painted speck you see is a single-cell algae.

Seaweed

Information

Large brown algae known as gulfweed grows in the colder water regions. Some types of brown algae have small air bladders that enable the plant to float in the water. These air bladders may be rounded like berries or elongated like a football. Masses of gulfweed float in the waters of the Atlantic making it difficult for ships attempting to pass through them. Giant brown kelp grows in the waters off the Pacific coasts of North and South America. The stems of the giant kelp may grow more than 200 feet (61 m) long.

Kelp has many commercial uses. Partially dried plants are used as fertilizer. Ground fine, kelp can be used as a body conditioner. Chemists extract iodine and algin from kelp. The latter keeps the water in milk from forming crystals in ice cream. Algin is used in salad dressings and aspirin.

Project

Create an exhibit of commercial products that contain seaweed and seaweed by-products.

Materials

- Permanent markers
- Self-sticking labels
- Table

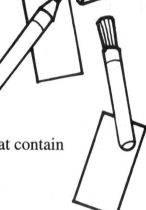

Directions

1. Look through kitchen cupboards and bathroom closets for products that contain seaweed or its by-products algin and iodine to bring to school.

2. Label each product with the student's name.

3. Prepare a tabletop exhibit that features all the categorized products.

3. Compare the findings. How many different commercial products were found? Take the exhibit apart after several days and return each product to its owner.

Plankton

Information

There are less than 100 species of plants in the ocean compared to some 250,000 flowering plants on land. Ocean plants can be found in the upper 100 feet (30 m) where they can get light and energy from the sun's rays. Because they live in the dense environment of water, ocean plants do not need roots to anchor them against the force of gravity. Instead, they drift along at the mercy of the ocean currents.

More than 99 percent of all plant life in the sea consists of a floating layer of microscopic particles called plankton. Although they cannot be seen with the naked eye, plankton are there by the millions, taking up nutrient salts and minerals directly from the sea water surrounding them. With the right environment—increasing hours of sunlight and ocean waters stirred by winter storms—they may double their numbers within two days.

Project

Conduct an experiment to observe and draw conclusions about the movement of plankton.

Directions

1. Fill the tub with water. Open the bag of bird seed (or other small item) and pour it into the water.

2. Stir the water with a spoon. Observe the movement of the "plankton" in relationship to the movement of the water.

3. Stir the water in different directions. Stir quickly. Stir slowly. What observations are made? What conclusions can be drawn about the movement of plankton in its ocean environment?

4. Unpot several potted plants and examine the roots. (Repot the plants when your investigations are concluded.) Discuss their purpose in the soil. How do rooted land plants compare to their rootless ocean counterparts?

Materials

- Large plastic tub
- Water
- Large spoons
- Bag of bird seed, popcorn kernels, or other small floatable items such as barley or dried peas
- Several potted plants

Diatoms

Information

One droplet of sea water under a microscope can reveal a world of *diatoms*—the largest group of plankton. These single-celled plants use the minerals in the sea to build a shiny, transparent framework of silica around them. Each diatom may look like anything from a pillbox to a golf tee with oddly-shaped projections that assist them in floating.

Floating alongside diatoms are *dinoflagellates*, one-celled living specks that are part plant, part animal. Like plants, they make their own food with the aid of the sun's energy. They move around under their own power like animals by means of whiplike tentacles with which they beat their way through the water. Dinoflagellates radiate luminescence. You cannot see them but you can see their light, a chemical reaction touched off by stormy seas.

Project

Recreate the framework of one-celled diatoms and dinoflagellates.

Materials

- Watercolor paint, brush
- Scissors
- Glue
- White construction paper
- Assorted recycled art materials such as buttons, yarn, construction, crepe and tissue paper scraps

Directions

1. Apply a wash of blue watercolor paint to construction paper. Allow to dry.

2. Create a world of diatoms on construction paper by cutting and gluing art materials in a variety of diatom and dinoflagellate shapes to cover the paper. Recreate the illustrations below on the chalkboard for ideas.

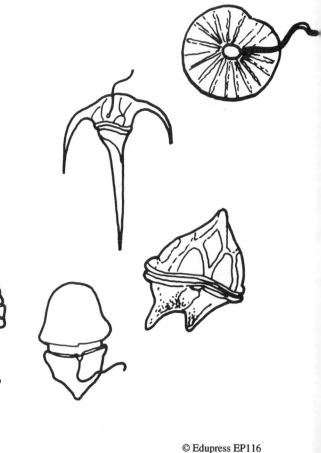

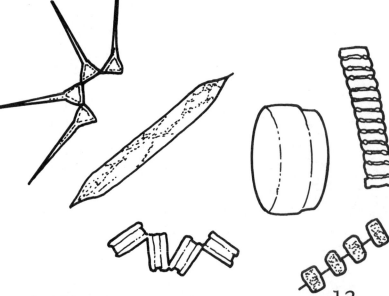

Animal Categories

Information

Ocean animals are divided into three groups: zooplankton—those that float; nekton—those that actively swim; and benthos—those that live on the shore, coral reefs, or the ocean bottom.

Zooplankton are wanderers. During the day they swim as deep as 600 feet (183 m) below the surface. At night, they rise to the upper levels of the water. Nekton are the ocean's travelers who move about freely. They travel to places where the food supply is abundant or to special areas to breed, lay eggs, or give birth. Whales make a 2,000 mile (3,218 km) round-trip from their winter breeding grounds to their summer feeding place! Benthos dwell on the bottom. Many are swimmers or walkers who move about for food but some stay in one position their entire life.

Project

Work in groups to create a quilt that features the variety of ocean life in each category.

Materials

- White construction paper squares
- Ocean Life Category Lists, following
- Crayons   • Reference books
- Tracing paper • Overhead projector (optional)

Directions

1. Divide into three groups. Give each group an Ocean Life Category List.

2. Each group member selects a different marine animal to color on a construction paper square. An overhead projector or tracing paper may be used to create more realistic drawings.

3. Assemble the squares on the classroom wall to create three different, colorful quilts. Label each quilt with the type of animal life pictured in it.

Nekton

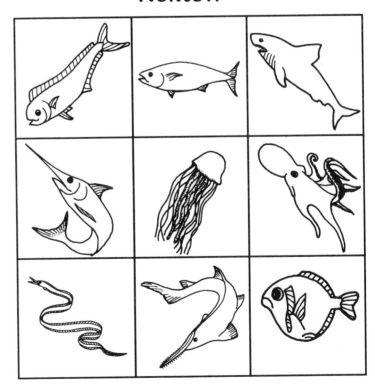

Animal Category Lists

Zooplankton

▼ Copepod   ▼ Jellyfish

▼ Arrowworm   ▼ Crab Larva

▼ Sea Gooseberry   ▼ Comb Jelly

▼ Dinoflagellate   ▼ Barnacle Larva

▼ Portuguese man-of-war

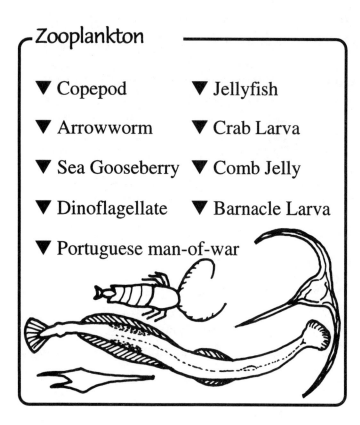

Within each of these categories there are many more varieties of ocean animals that are not listed.

Look through resource books to search for other interesting animals to feature on the quilts.

Among the dinoflagellates alone, there is a huge variety of shapes, all microscopic. They will need to be drawn many times their actual size for the quilt.

You may want to use tracing paper or an overhead projector to help you recreate the ocean animal you have chosen to draw.

Nekton

▼ Anchovy   ▼ Octopus

▼ Squid   ▼ Butterfly Fish

▼ Eel   ▼ Sea Lion

▼ Sailfish   ▼ Barracuda

▼ Whale   ▼ Shark

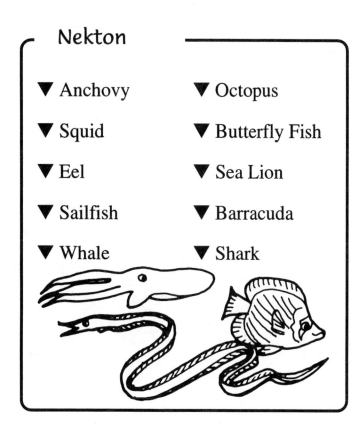

Benthos

▼ Sponge   ▼ Mussel

▼ Worm   ▼ Starfish

▼ Clam   ▼ Crab

▼ Oyster   ▼ Sea Anemone

▼ Coral   ▼ Sea Urchin

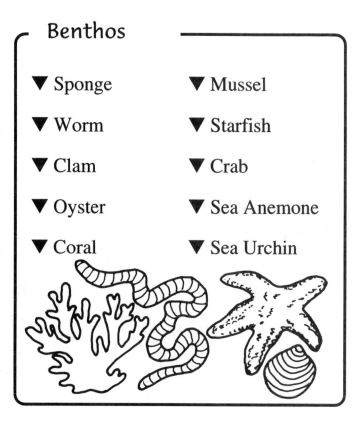

Fish

Information

Fish are boned animals that live in water. While they vary tremendously in size, shape, and color, they do have some features in common. All fish hatch from eggs, breathe through gills, have a backbone, and are *cold-blooded* (they cannot regulate their body temperature).

Many fish have an internal organ that allows them to adjust their buoyancy or ability to float. This organ is called the swim bladder, a balloon-like bag that fish can either inflate or deflate. The more the swim bladder inflates, the higher the fish rises in the water. When it deflates, the fish can sink to a deeper level of the ocean. By keeping just the right amount of air in the swim bladder, a fish can float in place. The swim bladder also enables a fish to move around slowly for short distances without swimming and using up its energy. Some fish, such as sharks, lack a swim bladder and must constantly swim in order to keep from sinking to the ocean bottom.

Project

Conduct a buoyancy experiment.

Materials

- Four zip-top bags
- Water
- Straw
- Bucket or bowl of water

Directions

1. Flatten one bag to completely remove the air inside. Close the seal.

2. Put a straw into the second bag and seal it along the top except where the straw protrudes. Blow into the straw to fill the bag with air. Remove the straw quickly and close the seal.

3. Fill a third bag half-filled with water, filling the remaining half with air by using the straw partially inserted into the bag as described in step #2 above.

4. Fill a fourth bag completely with water. Close the seal.

5. Fill the bucket or bowl with water. Put all the bags in the bucket of water and observe the results. Which floated the highest? Which floated the lowest? How do the results of the experiment relate to how high a fish floats in the water?

Fish Anatomy

Information

Most fish have a streamlined body. The head is somewhat rounded at the front. Fish do not have a neck. Their head connects directly to a trunk which narrows and blends into a tail. Fish have a variety of shapes. Some are torpedo-like. Some are flattened from side-to-side, others are flattened from top to bottom. Most have a tough skin with cells that produce a slimy mucus that makes them slippery and gives off an odor that we call "fishy." The color of most fish matches their surroundings. Fish have many features in common. Among these are scales, gills instead of lungs, and fins instead of legs. They also have a mouth, nostril, eyes, and tail.

Fish are vertebrates. But unlike those on land that need strong skeletons to counter gravity's force, simple ocean animals generally do not have strong muscular or skeletal support. While some fish are bonier than others, the skeleton of most consists of a skull, backbone, ribs, fin rays, jaw, and brain case.

Project

Complete a diagram of the external and internal anatomy of a fish.

Materials

- Fish Anatomy Diagrams, following two pages
- Transparency film
- Overhead projector
- Construction paper
- Pencil
- Crayons
- Glue

Directions

1. Reproduce the Fish Diagrams on white paper.

2. Review the external and internal anatomy by creating a transparency of the fish on this page and placing it on an overhead projector.

3. Discuss each feature as the diagrams are labeled. Color the external anatomy.

4. Mount the diagrams on construction paper as shown. Fold in half to create a standing display.

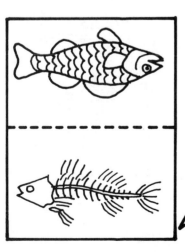

Fish External Anatomy

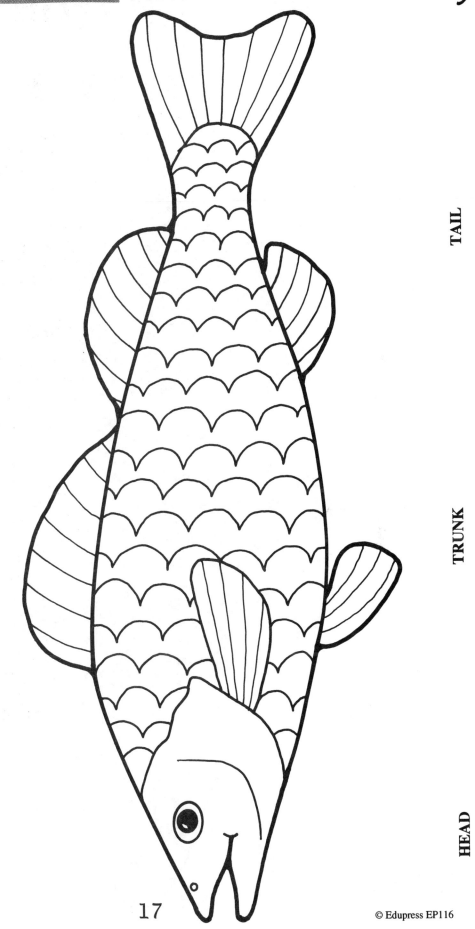

TAIL

TRUNK

HEAD

Label:
- mouth
- eye
- spiny dorsal fin
- gill cover
- anal fin
- nostril
- scales
- soft dorsal fin
- gill opening
- caudal fin

Ocean Life Activity Book

17

© Edupress EP116

Fish Internal Anatomy

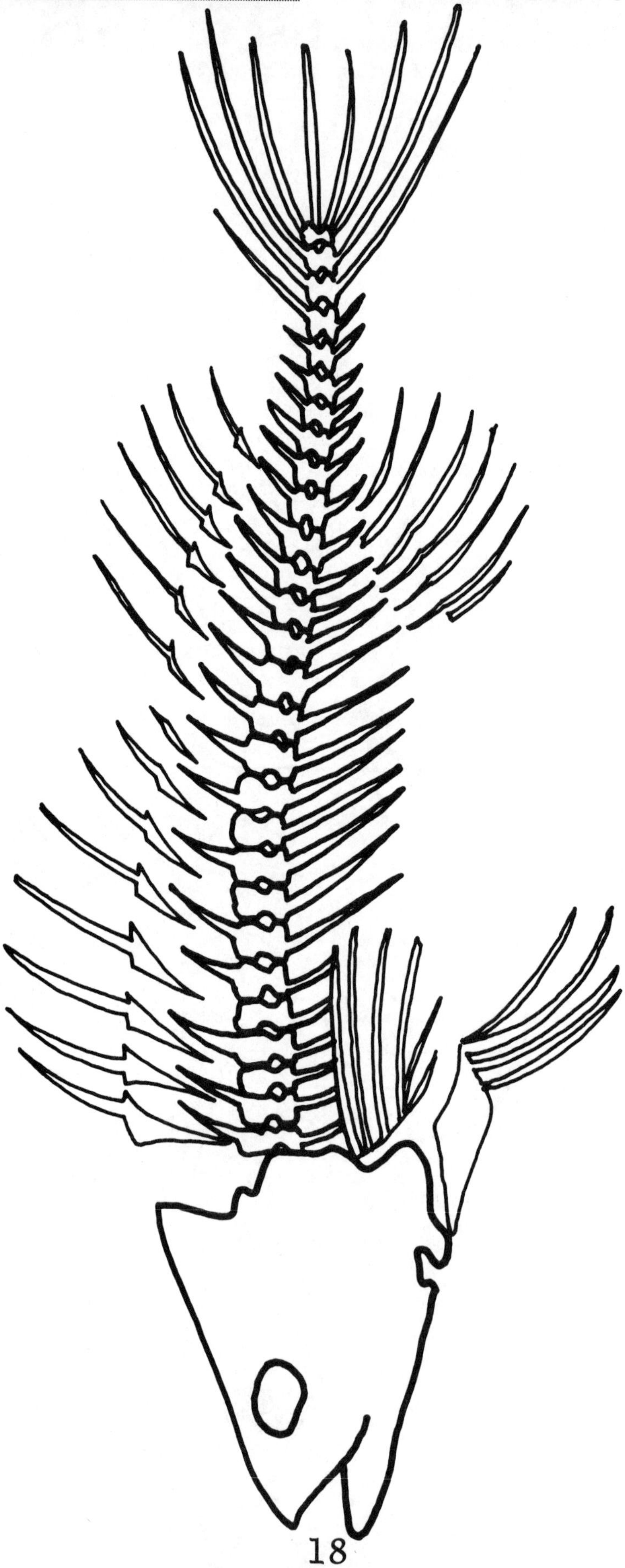

TAIL

TRUNK

HEAD

Label:
• backbone
• lower jaw
• brain case
• spiny fin rays
• fin ray support
• upper jaw
• rib
• anal spine
• soft fin ray

18

School of Fish

Information

Some species of fish live together in a group called a *school*. Many fish pack tightly together to create the illusion of one large mass. They move as one, turning together and darting through the water in a close formation that swims in unison without a leader. Schooling fish can be found all over the ocean. A school may consist of as few as 25 fish or hundreds of millions. All fish in a school are about the same size. Babies and adults are never in the same school. Some fish that form schools are tuna, herring, and sardines.

Schooling enables fish to combine their eyes and other senses to find food. When one member turns toward food, the rest turn with it. It also enables them to fool predators. If members of a school are spread out, the approach of a predator may bring them together so that they appear to be a single animal. Some predators, however, will careen into a school, cutting the fish to pieces.

Project

- Simulate a school of fish.
- Create a school of fish to hang from the classroom ceiling.

Materials

- Small drum or other rhythm instrument
- Whistle
- Playground
- Lots of children

Directions

1. Go outside with a large group of children—perhaps three or four classes. Discuss the rules of the simulation:
   - Try to stay in step with the slow beat of the rhythm instrument. Discuss the importance of a slow step in order to ensure safety.
   - At the sound of the whistle, turn left.

2. Practice in small groups. As proficiency of movement improves, merge the groups together until you have one large school.

3. If you are successful in moving as one unit, change the whistle signal to indicate left, right, and reverse.

School of Fish

Materials

- Tempera paint, any color
- Fish pattern, below
- Paint brush   • Scissors
- Hole punch   • Yarn

Directions

1. Reproduce the fish pattern. Each person should make four fish.

2. Paint the fish to look similar. Cut out when dry.

3. Punch a hole in the top and hang with yarn cut at different lengths.

4. Hang all the fish from the ceiling heading the same direction to create a school.

Fish Senses

Information

Like all vertebrates, fish have sense organs that tell them what is happening in their environment. Their hearing is keen, which enables them to locate prey by the noises they make when swimming or eating. Their sense of smell is excellent. Sharks can detect tiny traces of blood from a wounded fish from several hundred yards away. Their sight can detect moving objects even in fine light.

Fish have nerve endings that can transmit sensations only on their skin. It is doubtful they register pain as humans do. They have one line of sensitive cells that run along their side and detect changes in the flow of water, such as waves created by approaching predators. This also allows them to navigate in darkness. Scientists also believe fish taste with their whole bodies.

Project

Conduct investigations that compare five human senses to fish senses.

Directions

1. Set up testing stations with the necessary materials according to the list at right.

2. Reproduce copies of the Sense Comparison page, following. Discuss the information and brainstorm about the best ways to conduct comparison testing.

3. Divide into five or ten small working groups. One or two groups can be working on a sense investigation at one time. At a signal, the groups rotate to the next sense station. Groups may decide to conduct additional testing or improvise materials.

Materials

• Sense Comparison page, following
Sight
• Measuring tapes
Smell
• Strongly scented food
• Perfume
Taste
• Crackers (or other food) for taste tests
• Mirrors for examining the mouth
Touch
• Ice cubes
• Feather; items for sensory experience
Hearing
• Small bell or other sound instrument
• Buckets of water

Sight

Fish

• Can see to the right and left at the same time.

• Cannot see more than fifty feet (15.2 m).

• Cannot distinguish details or outlines.

• Has no eyelids; not sensitive to sunlight.

You

• _____

• _____

• _____

• _____

Smell

Fish

• Can identify another fish by its smell.

• Can smell something 100 yards (91.4 m) away.

• Can smell underwater.

• Has nostrils through which water can flow.

You

• _____

• _____

• _____

• _____

Taste

Fish

• Has taste buds in various parts of the mouth.

• Has taste buds on parts of their body.

• Tastes with the whole body.

• Can taste with whiskers around the mouth.

You

• _____

• _____

• _____

• _____

Touch

Fish

• Skin can feel very light pressure.

• Skin can feel changes in temperature.

• Can feel vibrations around them in their skin.

• Do not feel pain in muscles or other organs.

You

• _____

• _____

• _____

• _____

Hearing

Fish

• Have no outer ear.

• Can hear sounds produced in water.

• Can hear sounds above the water line.

• Sound is conducted by body tissues.

You

• _____

• _____

• _____

• _____

Fish Movement

Information

Ocean animals move in a variety of ways. Most fish have fins that move from side-to-side by means of muscles. Porpoises and whales use their strong, flexible tails to move up and down. Shape plays a role in how an ocean animal moves. Stingrays are shaped like flat disks. Their narrow edges enable them to slice easily through water. The fastest fish are the sailfish and swordfish whose torpedo-shaped snouts allow them to move at up to 60 miles (96.6 km) an hour.

An eel is narrow and uses a snake-like movement, enabling it to slip in and out of rocks and coral. Sea lions swim with their front flippers. Scallops flap their shells open then pull them closed. An octopus squeezes water from its body to create jet propulsion. Squids and jellyfish also move with jet propulsion.

Project

Play some outdoor games to simulate ocean animal movement.

Materials

- Frisbee®
- Jump rope

Directions

1. **Stingray Challenge**
   - Throw Frisbees® for speed and distance.
2. **Eel Escape**
   - Jump over a snaking rope and escape the giant eel.
3. **Flying Fish Contest**
   - Find out who can jump the highest.
4. **Crab Walk Relay**
   - Divide into teams and walk on "all fours" in a relay race.

Mammals

Information

Not all creatures in the ocean are fish. There are also mammals who spend their life in water. Ocean mammals include seals, whales, sea otters, porpoises, dolphins, and manatees. Some characteristics, such as a skeleton and internal organs, are similar to the characteristics of land mammals. Ocean mammals are warm-blooded. Females produce milk for their babies. Down through the ages, however, marine mammals have gradually lost many of the characteristics of other mammals. Their strong tail moves up and down to propel them through the water. Front legs have developed into flippers. They have no hind legs.

Water mammals have a developed brain and are among the most intelligent of all animals.

Project

Write and conduct an interview with an intelligent ocean mammal.

Materials

• Writing paper
• Pencil
• Resource books

Directions

1. Divide into cooperative groups. Imagine you are a news reporter who has been given the assignment to interview an intelligent ocean mammal.

2. Choose the subject of your interview.

3. Create a list of questions you would ask. Remember to include the who, what, where, when, why, and hows of good interviewing!

4. Conduct your interview. The "ocean mammals" who are interviewed—your classmates—must find the answer to the questions they cannot answer!

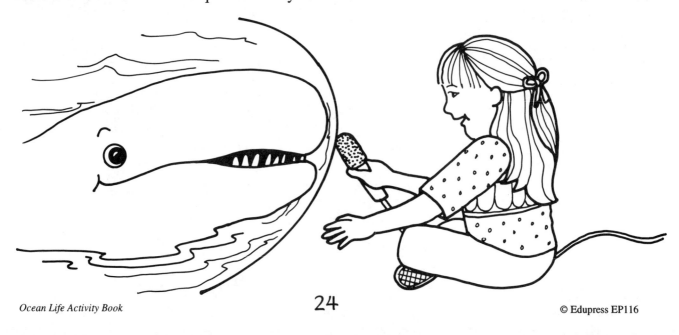

Whale

Information

A whale is not a fish; it is a mammal. Most whales are enormous. The blue whale, growing up to 100 feet (30 meters) long, is the largest animal that has ever lived. It is fortunate for the whale that water is dense. On land, a great blue whale would collapse under the weight of its 100-ton (91-metric ton) body. A whale has sideways tail fins and front flippers that allow it to steer and keep its balance. The only hair on its body is a few stiff strands on the head. It is a warm-blooded animal whose body temperature remains the same regardless of its surroundings.

Whales breathe by surfacing and inhaling air through their nostrils, or blowholes, on top of their heads. When a whale inhales, its huge lungs fill with more than 100 cubic feet (2.8 cubic meters) of air, enough to allow it to hold its breath for an hour or more while underwater.

Project

Conduct an experiment to compare the breath-holding ability of an ocean mammal to a land mammal's.

Materials

- Clock with a second hand
- Whale Ways fact-finding sheet, following

Directions

1. At a starting signal everyone takes a deep breath and holds it. Each person records the amount of time he can hold his breath before having to exhale.

2. Watch the clock for another 60 to 75 minutes, the length of time a whale can hold its breath underwater.

3. Reproduce the Whale Ways page. Complete the Whale Ways fact-finding research while you wait for the time to pass. Compare your breath-holding ability to a whale's!

Whale Ways

Scientists have identified at least 75 different types of whales. There are two major groups: baleen whales which do not have teeth and toothed whales, which have teeth. There are lots of interesting things to discover about whales, from the shape of their bodies to the hair on their heads.

Discover for yourself the many ways of the whale by working with a partner to complete this fact page.

Gray Whale

1.

2.

3.

Humpback Whale

1.

2.

3.

Sperm Whale

1.

2.

3.

Communication

Information

Many ocean creatures use sound to communicate. Whales and dolphins communicate with squeaks, clicks, grunts, whistles, and even tones or songs. In fact, sound travels so well through the water that whale songs can be heard for thousands of miles. Fish and shrimp also make a variety of clicks and grunts to locate one another or find prey. Dolphins use sound to locate prey by listening for echoes of the noises they make. Fish have a highly developed sense organ called the lateral line that picks up vibrations in the water. This helps them locate prey and avoid predators.

All ocean creatures need to be alert because sound travels five times faster in water than in air, about 5,000 feet (1,530 m) per second!

Project

Develop a form of communication based on sounds.

Materials

• Poster or butcher paper
• Marking pens

Directions

1. Work in a large group to create a new language based on sounds. Record your language on a large chart. For example, one click of the tongue may mean, "Let's go outside!" Two grunts may mean, "I'm hungry."

2. Develop at least 30 phrases and words to begin.

3. Imagine you are ocean creatures. Divide into pairs and try to communicate using the new sounds you created. Refer to the chart for help. Take turns "speaking" and translating the conversation.

1 squeak	= I want
3 quacks	= go
1 whistle	= food
3 kisses	= it's time
4 squeaks	= hurry
2 clicks	= sit down

Defense

Information

All ocean animals use inventive ways to defend themselves. *Protective coloration* plays an important role. Animals can change colors and camouflage themselves by blending in with the rocks or sand around them. Predators are blind to the color red so many fish are red as protection. Near the surface of well-lit waters animals are dark on top and light below, making it difficult for animals to see them from above looking down into dark water or from below looking up toward light. Streamlined fish swim away at top speed when they sense danger.

Some ocean animals have long tentacles covered with powerful stinging cells. Bottom-living creatures dig into the mud or hide in rocks and seaweed. Crabs and lobsters have hard shells and strong claws. Parrot fish spend every night inside slimy bags that taste so unpleasant no other ocean creature will bother them. Squid squeeze out clouds of ink to hide themselves as they flee a predator. Cowries shoot acid, starfish will abandon an arm, and crabs will break off a claw in order to escape.

Project

Create a sandwich board and present an oral report while assuming the identity of an ocean animal.

Materials

- Poster board
- Scissors
- Construction paper
- Assorted art materials
- Butcher paper
- Glue
- Tissue paper
- Paint

Directions

1. Select an ocean animal to research. Find out at least ten interesting facts about this animal including where it lives in the ocean, how it moves, how it defends itself, its size, shape, and color.

2. Use butcher paper or poster board to create a two-sided sandwich board decorated to resemble the selected animal. Be creative in the use of materials. Connect the sandwich boards with butcher paper straps at the top. Be sure the board fits over the head.

3. Assume the role of the animal and present an oral report telling all about yourself. Classmates may ask questions following the oral report.

Mollusks

Information

Mollusks make up the largest group of water animals. There are about 100,000 known kinds of living mollusks and scientists find about 1,000 new species every year. Most mollusks have a hard armor-like shell that protects a boneless soft body. All have a skin-like organ called a mantle which produces the substance that makes the shell. The edges of the mantle squeeze out liquid shell materials and add them to the shell as the mollusk grows.

There are six classes of mollusks. *Univalve* is the largest class and includes limpets, slugs, snails, and whelks. *Bivalve* is the second largest class and includes clams, oysters, mussels, and scallops. Octopuses and squid, the most active class of mollusks, have no external shell. The remaining three classes are tooth shells, chitons, and the extremely rare Monoplacophora, which are found only in the deepest parts of the ocean.

Project

Conduct observations, experiments, and demonstrations to gain an understanding of mollusks.

Materials

• As described for each mollusk on this and the following two pages

---

Univalve

Although some univalves such as sea slugs have no shells, most have a single coiled shell into which its soft body (which acts like muscular foot) can withdraw when threatened. Univalves gather food with a long ribbon-like tongue called a radula that has many tiny teeth on it.

Project: Observe the features of the land snail to understand its counterpart in the ocean.

Materials
• Garden snails   • Magnifying glass

Directions
1. Collect garden snails for observation activities.

2. Observe and simulate the movement of its muscular foot. Examine the shell and record how the snail uses it for protection. Place a leaf in front of the snail and observe how it gathers and chews food.

29

Mollusks

Bivalves have two shells held together by hinges. When an enemy is near, the shell clamps shut and can stay closed for as long as several weeks. Most bivalves have no head or teeth. They move by pushing a strong foot into the mud and pulling themselves along.

Project: Create a bivalve with your hands to demonstrate its parts and functions.

Materials
- Hands
- Piece of soft sponge

Directions
1. Place the sponge (the bivalve's soft body) in the palm of one hand. Cup both hands together. Open and close them at the fingertips, keeping the wrists joined, to simulate the movement of a bivalve.

2. Divide into pairs. Take turns trying to pry open closed "bivalves."

Chiton

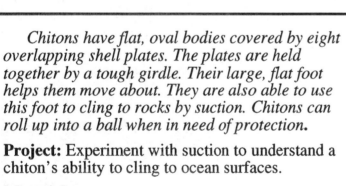

Chitons have flat, oval bodies covered by eight overlapping shell plates. The plates are held together by a tough girdle. Their large, flat foot helps them move about. They are also able to use this foot to cling to rocks by suction. Chitons can roll up into a ball when in need of protection.

Project: Experiment with suction to understand a chiton's ability to cling to ocean surfaces.

Materials
- Small suction cups (available in hardware stores)

Directions
1. Draw conclusions about the force of a chiton's suction by applying the suction cups to wet, underwater, or different textured surfaces. To which does the suction cup adhere most successfully? How could a chiton be loosened from its hold on a rock?

Mollusks

Octopuses and Squid

Octopuses and squid have dome-shaped heads and long tentacle arms covered with suction disks. Octopuses have eight tentacles and squid have ten. They use their tentacles to capture prey and pull it into their jaws. These mollusks are able to change color and squirt an inky fluid to escape from enemies.

An octopus has no bones and no inside shell. A tough protective wrapper called a mantle covers the body and gives it shape.

Project: Conduct an experiment to explore the purpose of an octopus' mantle.

Materials
- 1 cup (236 ml) flour
- 1 cup (236 ml) water
- Bowl
- Large spoon
- Paper plate
- Zip-top bags
- Small paper cups
- Small containers of various shapes

Directions

1. Mix flour and water together to create a runny paste. Imagine this is the boneless body of an octopus.

2. Spoon some of the paste mixture onto a paper plate. What happens?

3. Now spoon some paste mixture into a small zip-top bag. This is the octopus' mantle. What differences are observed? Manipulate the shape of the bag with your hands. Record your observations.

4. Continue to experiment with the paste mixture and containers of varying rigidity. What conclusions can be drawn about the mantle of an octopus based on recorded observations?

Shells

Information

There are about 100,000 kinds of mollusk shells. The smallest, that of a sea snail, are the size of a grain of sand. The largest, that of the giant clam, may measure four feet (1.2 m) long and weigh 500 pounds (230 kg). As a mollusk grows, its shell grows. Most shells have an outer, middle, and inner layer that contain calcium carbonate, a kind of limestone found in rocks. The food eaten by a mollusk provides the minerals that form the shell and give it color. The inner layer may be produced as a shiny substance known as mother-of-pearl.

Each shell has its own special design and shape. Univalves have an opening at one end. Snails grow their shells in a clockwise direction. Keyhole limpets have a hole in the center. Bivalves have two matching shells that often pull apart after the animal inside has departed. Tooth shells look like long needles or miniature elephant tusks. Chitons have eight separate, movable pieces that look like tiny suits of armor.

Project

Create a shell exhibit.

Materials

- Bags
- Large, shallow-sided gift or shirt boxes
- Shell stickers or other decorations
- Tempera paint
- Self-sticking labels
- Books about shells
- Paper towels
- Magnifying glass
- Tape
- Marking pens

Alternative materials—(see directions)
- Crayons, colored pencils
- Scissors

Directions

If you live near an ocean:

1. Take a walk along the beach. Carry a bag in which to place the shells you collect.

2. Carefully rinse the shells. Lay them on paper towels to dry.

3. Decorate the box with paint and stickers.

4. Examine the shells. Look through books and identify each one. Create a label that includes the name of the mollusk and its shell group (bivalve, etc.). Tape the shell inside the box with the label below it.

If you DON'T live near an ocean (or didn't collect many shells):

1. Find colored pictures of shells in resource books or on the Internet. Use colored pencils or crayons to illustrate the shells. Cut out and mount the pictures in the box as described in step #4 above.

Crustaceans

Information

Crustaceans, a special class of arthropod, are shellfish, but they are different from mollusks. A hard shell called an *exoskeleton* covers a crustacean's body and protects its internal organs. The body of an adult crustacean has three parts—head, thorax, abdomen—each of which consists of many jointed segments that make them very flexible. Most crustaceans have six to 14 pairs of legs used for swimming, walking, or as pincers for catching food, fighting, or other activities. Barnacles, crabs, crayfish, shrimp, and lobsters are examples of crustaceans.

The shell does not grow along with the crustacean's body. As a lobster, crab, or shrimp grows, it must shed its shell in order to make a bigger one with room to grow into. The new shell takes a week or two to harden. During this time the animal is helpless and unprotected.

Project

Create a paper model of a giant spider crab. Experiment with tweezers to simulate crustacean pincers.

Materials

To make one Giant Crab:
- Giant Crab pattern, following
- Half-sheet red poster board
- Black crayons
- Tissue paper
- Tweezers
- Scissors
- Stapler
- 22 metal brads
- Hole punch

Directions

1. Reproduce the Giant Crab pattern. Cut out the pattern pieces. Lay them on red poster board. Trace around each one and cut them out. Continue to trace and cut until you have as many of each pattern piece as indicated on the pattern page.

2. Staple the two body parts together. Stuff lightly with tissue. Glue the long legs to the body, five per side. Use a brad to join a short leg to the long and a long leg to the short at the dot. You may want to use a hole punch first.

4. Connect pincers to the two front legs. Count the leg joints. Compare the number to the human body.

5. Experiment with tweezers as implements for picking up objects. Draw conclusions about the dexterity of a crustacean. What types of food would one be able to eat?

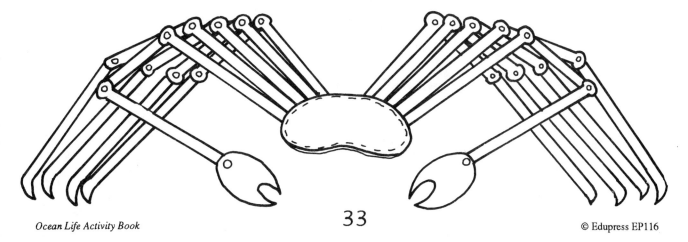

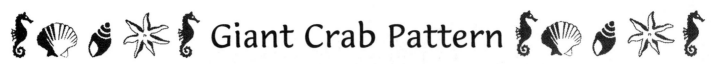

Giant Crab Pattern

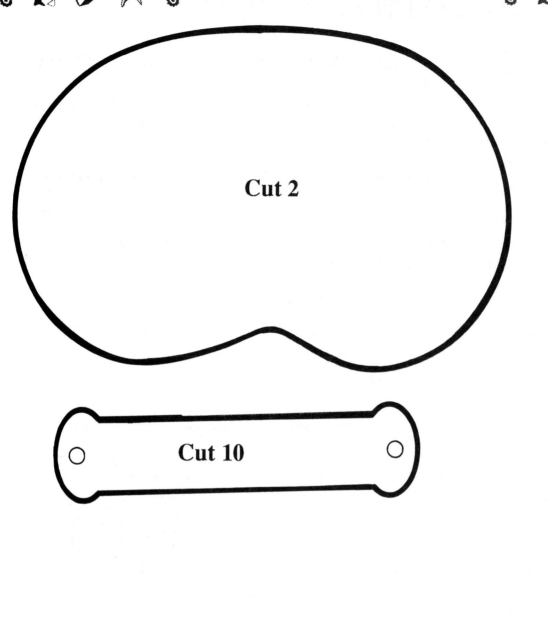

Cut 2

Cut 10

Cut 20

Cut 2

Echinoderms

Information

Starfish, brittle stars, sand dollars, sea urchins, and sea cucumbers creep slowly along the sea floor and among the rocks in search of food. They are a part of the group of ocean animals called *echinoderms*. There are about 5,000 different kinds of echinoderms.

Echinoderms have *radial symmetry*. Their body parts are arranged around the center of the animal like the spokes of a wheel around the hub. Echinoderm bodies are usually divided into five sections around the center with the mouth in the center of the underside. Most echinoderms have tube feet projecting from the body. The tubes are used for moving, feeding, breathing, and sensing.

Some echinoderms have spines that grow from a limestone shell which lies just under the skin. These spines assist the animal with crawling and digging.

Project

- Craft echinoderm models from clay to reinforce the concept of radial symmetry.
- Create a table top exhibit.

Materials

- Echinoderm Information Cards, following
- Self-hardening clay
- Clay paint
- Brushes
- Measuring tape or ruler
- Additional materials as noted for each echinoderm

Directions

1. Reproduce several pages of the Echinoderm Information Cards. Cut apart the cards and give one to each student.

2. Discuss the concept of radial symmetry. Use the description and illustration on each card as a guide to craft the echinoderm described from clay.

3. Create a tabletop exhibit. Group echinoderms by type. Assign the students who created each type to take charge of the table. Invite visitors to attend your exhibit. Students at each table should be prepared to provide interesting information about the echinoderm they crafted.

Echinoderm Information Cards

SEA CUCUMBER

▼ DESCRIPTION— A sea cucumber has a cylinder-shaped body that looks like a cucumber. Its mouth is at one end of its body. There are five double-rows of tube feet on the body. Most grow less than one foot (30 cm) long.

▼ CRAFT TOOLS—Real cucumber for reference!

SAND DOLLAR

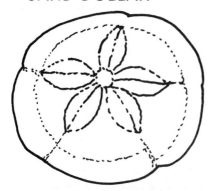

▼ DESCRIPTION— A sand dollar lives in shallow coastal waters. Its thin, flat, circular body is two to four inches (5 to 10 cm) wide. It looks somewhat like a silver dollar or a cookie. The top has a set of breathing tubes that are arranged in the form of a five-point star. Its mouth is on its underside.

▼ CRAFT TOOLS—Rolling pin, star-shaped pattern to press into upper surface

STARFISH

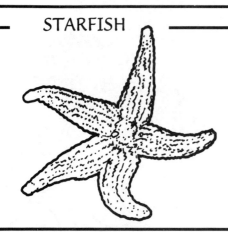

▼ DESCRIPTION— Also called a sea star, a starfish has arm-like extensions on its body. Most have five arms and look somewhat like five-pointed stars. Others have many arms and are called sun stars because they resemble the sun and its rays. Its mouth is in the middle of its underside. Rows of slender disks line grooves on its body.

▼ CRAFT TOOLS—Star-shaped cookie cutter, rolling pin

SEA URCHIN

▼ DESCRIPTION— A sea urchin is shaped like a ball and is covered with long movable spines. Its mouth is at the center of its lower surface. Body wastes leave through an opening in the center of its upper surface.

▼ CRAFT TOOLS—Toothpicks

Coelenterates

Information

There are about 9,000 species of *coelenterates* and most of them live in the sea. Coelenterate comes from Greek words meaning "hollow intestine." The soft-bodied coelenterate may be shaped like a cylinder, a bell, or an umbrella. Its body wall has two layers, one that makes up the body covering and a second inner layer that lines the large digestive cavity.

Coelenterates include jellyfish, sea anemones, and corals. A jellyfish has tentacles with special stinging cells. Smaller ocean animals sometimes take refuge inside these hanging tentacles. A polyp is a coelenterate with a body shaped like a hollow cylinder. A polyp lives with one end of its body attached to the sea bottom. The mouth and tentacles are on the other end. They may exist singly or may live together in colonies. Sea anemones are single polyps. Coral polyps usually form colonies.

Project

- Make an edible jellyfish and explore the concept of translucence.
- Create a lacy coral reef.

Materials

- As listed for Coelenterate Projects, following
- Ocean life resource books

Directions

1. Choose one or both coelenterate projects to complete. Gather the necessary materials.
2. Look through resource books for additional pictures of coral reefs in order to recreate the colors.

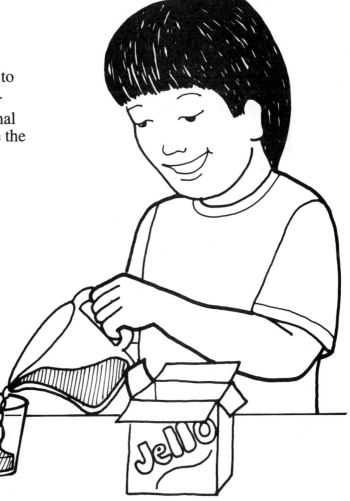

Coelenterates

Jellyfish are primitive animals without skeletons, eyes, or brains. Poisonous tentacles hang from a translucent, umbrella-shaped body. Jellyfish vary in color from pink to blue or yellow. Sometimes they are striped! They propel forward by squeezing their bodies to push out water below.

Project: Make an edible jellyfish and learn about translucence.

Materials
- Lemon or lime gelatin mix
- Clear plastic cups
- Mixing bowls
- Spoons
- Ladle
- Paper plates

Directions

1. Mix gelatin according to package directions. Ladle a small amount into plastic cups and chill to set. Unmold the set gelatin onto a paper plate. Examine the translucence by placing an object on one side of the gelatin and looking through it. How would translucence make jellyfish difficult to sea in the ocean?

2. Eat the jellyfish!

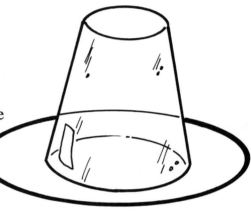

Coral

Corals are tiny animals which build their own external skeletons of lime from the sea water. The skeletons form the foundation of ridges in the sea called reefs. Coral takes on many irregular shapes in shades of tan, orange, yellow, purple, and green.

Project: Create a paper coral reef.

Materials

- Tissue paper in various colors
- Scissors
- Glue diluted with water
- Paint brush
- Construction paper

Directions

1. Fold and cut tissue paper to create a snowflake effect. Lay the tissue in a colorful, overlapping design on the construction paper to create a coral reef. Dip the brush into the glue/water mixture and paint over the tissue to secure it to the construction paper.

Sponges

Information

Sponges live on the ocean bottom attached to rocks or shells. The sponge does not resemble any other animal. Most have no definite shape. Some are thin and flat. Others are round and vase-like. A sponge has no head, mouth, or internal organs. It depends on a system of water canals in its body to bring in food and oxygen and carry away waste products. Tiny pores in the surface lead to thousands of canals. The canals join a network of smaller canals that eventually lead to the outside.

Sponges have several types of skeletons. Some are made of tiny hard needles. Others are soft and elastic. They have remarkable powers of regeneration. Even if much of the body breaks away, the sponge can replace the broken parts. Sponges are incredibly absorbent and make excellent cleaning tools. Most sponges sold in stores are not true sponges but are made of synthetic material made to look and to clean like true ocean sponges.

Project

Conduct demonstrations using store-bought commercial sponges.

Materials

• Sponges from the market
• Water
• Soap
• Towels
• Measuring cup

Directions

1. Demonstrate the ability of a sponge to absorb liquids by soaking it in water then squeezing the water into a measuring cup.

2. Demonstrate the cleaning ability of a sponge by scrubbing away dirt in the classroom or other area of the school.

3. Compare the results of each demonstration. What properties of a sponge were demonstrated?

Food Chain

Information

Ocean animals are linked by food chains that make all ocean creatures dependent upon each other. The marine food chain is similar to a pyramid. The few largest creatures at the top could not exist without the layers of increasingly smaller animals below it. Tiny animals eat microscopic plant life and use the nutrients for their own growth. These small animals become food for larger animals. As one animals eats another these nutrients are passed along to each animal.

A hump-backed whale needs as many as 5,000 herring in its stomach to feel comfortably full. A herring may have 6,000 small crustaceans in its stomach, each of which contains as many as 130,000 diatoms in its stomach. Some four hundred billion diatoms sustain a single medium-sized whale for only a few hours!

Project

Cut and paste pictures to create a marine food chain pyramid.

Materials

- Food Chain Pyramid pattern, following
- Ocean Life patterns, pages 7-8
- Scissors
- Crayons
- Glue

Directions

1. Reproduce the Ocean Life pattern pages and the Food Chain Pyramid pattern page.

2. Consider the size of each animal in the patterns. These sizes are reflected in the pattern drawings. Cut out each animal. Arrange it into its logical place on the pyramid with the smallest animals at the bottom.

3. Glue the pictures in place on the pyramid. You may find that some of your placement choices will need to be changed as you continue your ocean life study!

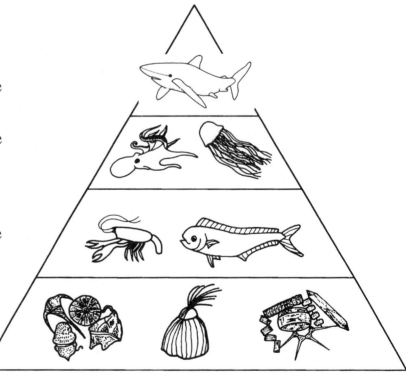

Food Chain Pyramid

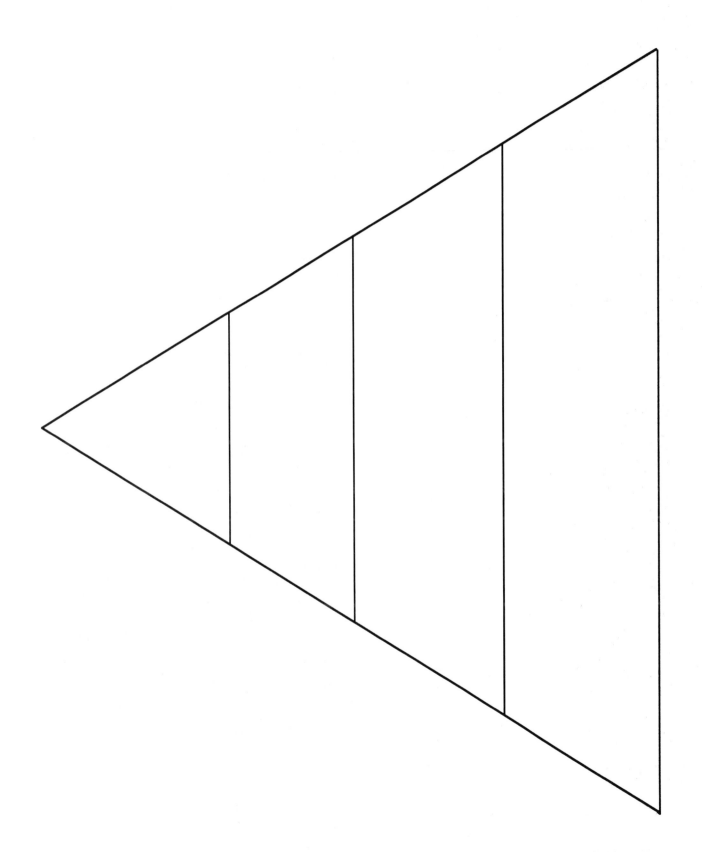

Food From the Sea

Information

The ocean is an important source of food. Fisheries supply about ten percent of the world's animal protein. Forms of preservation such as canning and drying enable people all over the world to sample food from the sea, but generally people eat what is easily available to them. Seaweeds are eaten in the Orient as a vegetable and a relish. Dried seaweed, sold in papery sheets, is considered a tasty snack. Eggs scooped from the prickly shells of sea urchins are a delicacy.

In most parts of the world, mollusks are eaten every day. The most popular kinds are clams, oysters, and scallops. Crustaceans such as lobster and crab are favorites as well. The bonier the fish, the less likely it is to be a popular food fish.

Project

Find out what seafood is available in your area. Conduct a seafood sampling activity.

Materials

- Menus from local restaurants
- Grocery store advertisements
- Writing paper
- Affordable seafood such as canned tuna, seaweed (international food section of the market)

Directions

1. Read menus and advertisements from local restaurants and grocery stores. Locate the seafood products. Make a list of those available where you live. Rank them in order of cost. Determine which are the most affordable. Why are some more expensive than others?

2. Ask parents and the local fish grocers to contribute some samples for a classroom tasting activity.

Marine Biologists

Information

Marine biologists study life in the sea. They try to discover how ocean organisms develop and grow, how their bodies function, how they get food, and how they live in relation to other marine plants and animals. Marine biologists use organisms from the sea in laboratory experiments to produce substances that are valuable to human beings. Their work has resulted in the discovery of substances that can be used in treating viral and bacterial infections, cancer, skin infections, food and blood poisoning, and pneumonia.

Biological oceanographers try to find out how marine organisms live in relationship to each other. They trace how they evolved, how the body organs work, and how they can function in the darkness of the underwater world. Their laboratory is on an ocean-going vessel, using scuba diving equipment and electronic equipment to assist them in their explorations.

Project

Simulate the role of a marine biologist or biological oceanographer. Hold a news conference to announce an important discovery about life in the ocean.

Materials

• Materials as needed by each group

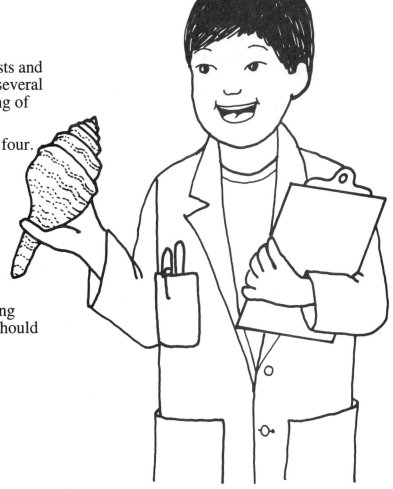

Directions

1. Discuss the different types of ocean scientists and the kinds of research they conduct. Watch several newscasts together to gain an understanding of the presentation style.

2. Divide into cooperative groups of three or four.

3. Allow time for each group to:
   • Research pertinent information
   • Fabricate a discovery
   • Assemble their materials
   • Design appropriate costumes
   • Create and practice a presentation

5. Each group of scientists is responsible for holding a news conference about an exciting discovery in the underwater world. They should relate how their information was obtained (observation, experimentation, etc.).

Sea Monsters

Information

Ships' logs and sailors' tales tell of sightings and frightening encounters with sea monsters and serpents. But these tales are based on ignorance, superstition, and unproven information. While ocean-going research vessels have picked up echoes from very large moving bodies on sonar equipment, none have ever been seen or located.

It is true that there are monster-sized creatures in the sea. Whales, giant squid, and sharks are counted among them. They can also be monster-like in their attacks. The most dangerous are man-eating sharks. Barracuda have razor-sharp teeth. Killer whales have a fearsome reputation. Sea snakes, while not truly a serpent at only six feet (1.8 m) long, have a poison more deadly than a cobra's. The deadly poison of a jellyfish tentacles have been know to kill a person in a matter of a few seconds.

Project

Write a fictional tale about an encounter with a "sea monster."

Materials

• Monster Tales page, following
• Pencil
• Construction paper
• Stapler

Directions

1. Discuss the important elements of a fictional story. Propose some plots and characters. Practice writing descriptive sentences.

2. Duplicate Monster Tales page and distribute to the class.

3. Write a fictional tale about an encounter with a sea monster.

4. Illustrate the story. Bind it in a construction paper cover.

Monster Tales

Speaking of the Ocean ...

People often refer to ocean life when they speak but what exactly do they mean?
Interview three different people and you'll probably get three different responses.
Record them here; then share them with classmates.

Share a "pearl of wisdom."

1. _____
2. _____
3. _____

Describe something that makes you "clam up."

1. _____
2. _____
3. _____

What makes someone a "real crab?"

1. _____
2. _____
3. _____

When do you have a "whale of a time?"

1. _____
2. _____
3. _____

Glossary Game

Here's an easy game to make to have on hand
for instant learning fun—and to build ocean life vocabulary!

Go Fish

Materials
- Go Fish Playing Cards, below
- Blue construction paper
- Tape
- Scissors
- Large plastic container
- Marking pen

Directions
1. Cut the top off the plastic container. Decorate the container with blue paper waves.

2. Reproduce and cut apart the playing cards. Write a glossary word on each one. Put the cards in the plastic container.

Playing Rules
- Divide into teams.
- One player fishes for a card, reads the glossary word, and says the definition aloud.
- Score one point for each correct definition.

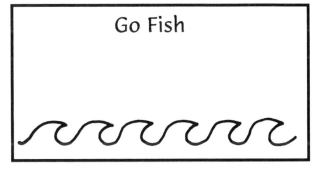

World Wide Web

Search on the world wide web to expand your knowledge of the ocean and the fascinating variety of life that inhabits it. Keep in mind that web pages change constantly. The web pages below were active at publication date but their continued presence is not guaranteed. The amount of knowledge available to enthusiastic "divers" is as vast as the oceans of the world.

Address	Content
oceanlink.island.net	*Oceanlink*—Here you'll find information about marine science topics like oceanography, marine biology, marine mammals, marine pollution, and much more!
www.whoi.edu/	*Woods Hole Oceanographic Institute*—A world of organized general information presented by a recognized leader in the field of oceanography.
www.seasky.org/seas.html	*Sea and Sky: Reef Life*—Explore the life that abounds in a coral reef. Weblinks to information on marine mammals, sea reptiles, and sharks.
www.well.com/user/bridge/index.html	*Marine Mammals Home Page*—Information on endangered marine mammals: dolphins, porpoises, sea lions, seals, whales, and walruses.
ourworld.compuserve.com/homepages/jaap/	*Marine Mammals*—Images and information about dolphins, whales, sea lions, walruses, seals, and fish.